CUFF, A Baby Bear

Cuff was born during the winter in a den on a woodland hillside. After he was able to stand on his feet, he found he could also climb a tree. Soon he discovered the joy of eating honey and the pain of a bee sting! Meeting some picnickers, he learns that young bears and young people may have fun playing together, but mothers of both disapprove. Cuff has other adventures, some very dangerous ones, but he survives his first year. When he returns with his mother to their winter sleeping den, he is five times bigger than he was when he stumbled out on his weak new legs.

A **SEE** AND **READ** BOOK

CUFF
A Baby Bear
Virginia Frances Voight

Illustrated by SALEM TAMER

G. P. Putnam's Sons New York

Library of Congress Catalog Card Number: 68-24553

PRINTED IN THE UNITED STATES OF AMERICA

06209

The spring sunshine was warm and bright. It melted the snow on the hillside, where the black bear had her den. Sunbeams danced into the den to wake the mother bear. She lifted her head and sniffed the air.

The air smelled of green plants. It told the bear that now there was food for her in the woodland. It was time to leave the den, where she had slept all winter.

She crawled out between the rocks that made a doorway to the den.

Cuff, her cub, crawled after her. He was little and fat, with soft black fur and eyes like bright buttons.

He had been born during the winter,
deep in the darkness of the den. He had
never seen sunshine or trees. He did not
know that there were other animals in the
world.

He peeped out of the doorway. The
bright sunshine made him blink his eyes,
but it felt good on his face.

His mother was eating grass. This was
her first food in four months. She saw Cuff
and woofed for him to come outside.

Cuff had never done any walking. His legs were as shaky as jelly. He pushed himself out of the den on his stomach.

Outside, he tried to stand. His legs would
not hold him up. Bump! He sat down hard.
He bawled like a hurt baby.

His mother nosed him gently to his feet.

She walked away and woofed for him to
follow. Cuff took only a few steps before
he fell down again.

Wah! he bawled.

His mother woofed sharply. She had
called her cub, and he had to obey her!
This is the first lesson that all young
animals learn.

Cuff got to his feet again. His mother waited until he walked slowly to her side. She licked his face, and then she let him nurse.

Cuff kept on trying to walk. He fell
down a few times, but with every step his
legs grew stronger.

Tap, tap, tap. A woodpecker was tapping
on a tree nearby. Cuff hid behind his
mother. The woodpecker was the first bird
he had seen. He didn't know what to
make of it.

A squirrel began to talk to him from a branch overhead. Cuff almost jumped out of his skin in surprise. He woofed at the squirrel. He wanted it to come down and play. The squirrel ran away through the treetops.

Most mother bears have two or three
cubs at a time, but Cuff was an only child.
He was lonely for a playmate. He pawed
at his mother and nipped her ears with his
tiny teeth. He wanted her to play with
him, but she was still sleepy. She stretched
out for a nap in the sun.

A rabbit came hopping through the woods. Cuff woofed eagerly. Perhaps this long-eared animal would play with him! The rabbit hopped away, and Cuff took off after it.

When Cuff's mother awoke, she looked
around for Cuff. He was nowhere in sight!
Bears have sharp ears and noses. Cuff's
mother sniffed the air. The wind carried
Cuff's special smell to her. Now she knew
where to look for him.

Although she was so big and heavy, she could gallop as fast as a horse. She ran to where the wind said she would find Cuff. There he was! The rabbit had run away. Cuff was playing with a hoptoad.

Cuff's mother was angry because he had not stayed near her. She cuffed him hard. Cuff howled, but she spanked him all the way back to the den.

Grown bears are so big and strong that they have nothing to fear in the woods. But a bear cub is in danger from male bears and other animals. Little Cuff was safe only when he was with his mother.

His mother led him to a tree and gave
him a gentle push with her nose. Bear
cubs take to climbing as quickly as baby
turtles take to swimming. Cuff hugged the
tree with his front paws. He dug into the
bark with the claws on his back feet and
pushed hard. Up he went!

At first he climbed slowly, but soon he could fairly gallop up a tree. He sat on a high branch that rocked in the wind. It was like a bear cub swing!

Now his mother could leave him in a
tree while she looked for food. But she
never went far away.

One morning Cuff's mother led him away from the den. She was looking for a wild bees' nest. At last she found a hollow tree with a hole high in the trunk. Bees were flying in and out, so she knew that there was a nest inside.

She made Cuff stay on the ground while
she climbed the tree.

Cuff watched his mother pull a big
piece of honeycomb out of the bees' nest.
It was dripping with honey. She stuffed
the comb into her mouth and ate it. There
were bees on the comb. She ate them, too.

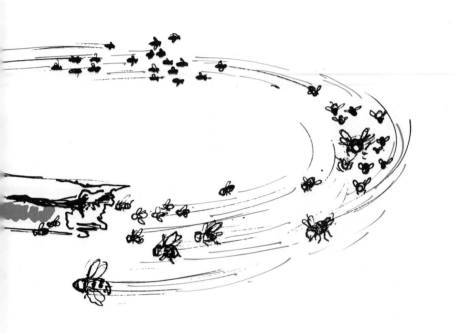

A cloud of bees poured out of the nest.
Buzzing with anger, they flew around the
bear. They tried to sting her, but their
stings would not go through her fur. She
ate some bees that crawled on her paws.

A bit of honeycomb fell to the ground.
Cuff sniffed it and licked it. The sticky
sweet stuff tasted good!

His mother was backing down the tree.
The cloud of angry bees buzzed along with
her. A bee lit on Cuff's nose and stung him.

Wah! Cuff howled. His nose burned like fire.

His mother took him to a muddy spot on the shore of a pond. He pushed his nose into the cool mud. The mud took the hurt out of the bee sting.

35

8374

The bears swam about to wash their
sticky fur. When they went ashore, Cuff's
mother took a nap. Cuff walked along the
shore, looking for hoptoads. Soon he was
out of sight of his sleeping mother.

Farther along the shore a tourist family had stopped for lunch. Mr. Dale parked the car beside the road and spread a blanket under the trees. The children, Kathy and Joe, raced down to the pond.

"Polliwogs," Joe said, pointing in the water.

Mrs. Dale opened the lunch basket.
"Kathy, Joe!" she called.

Joe took a sandwich and some cookies
and went back to the pond. He put his
cookies on a rock. He took bites of his
sandwich while he watched the polliwogs.

The rest of the family finished lunch and put the things back in the car.

"Come on, Joe!" Kathy called. "It's time to go."

No one noticed Cuff coming along the shore.

Suddenly Cuff stopped and sniffed the air. What was it that smelled so good? His nose led him to the rock where Joe had left the cookies. He pawed at a cookie and ate it. It tasted like honey!

Just then Joe turned around. "Hey!" he
shouted. "Those are mine!"

He wasn't a bit afraid of the fat little
cub. He snatched the rest of the cookies
from under Cuff's nose.

Cuff wasn't afraid either. To him, Joe
was just another animal cub. He pawed at
Joe's hands to get the cookies. Joe laughed.
He gave Cuff a cookie and ate one himself.

Up on the road, Mr. Dale told Kathy to
go after Joe.

"He must still be watching the polliwogs," she said.

But when she saw Cuff, she gave a little
scream. "Joe is playing with a bear cub!"

Her father started down to the pond at
a run. "I hope its mother isn't around."

"Joe! Come away from that bear!" Mrs. Dale called.

All these noisy, running people frightened Cuff.

Wah! he bawled. *Wahhhh!*

He sounded as if he had been hurt.

Up the pond shore his mother was
awake and looking for him. Her sharp ears
heard his cry.

Roarrr! Her answer meant, "I'm coming,
little son, and I'll fix whoever is hurting
you!"

"Hear that?" cried Mr. Dale. "We've got to get away from here!" He snatched Joe up. "Everyone inside the car!"

Through the closed windows of the car, they saw Cuff's mother galloping along the shore. She looked big and fierce and angry. Kathy moved closer to her father.

"I've read that a grown bear can tear the doors off a car."

"That's true," her father said. "But we won't let her get that close."

They watched the big bear run up to her cub. She nosed him all over to make sure that he was not hurt.

Now that his mother was there, Cuff
was no longer frightened. He ate a cookie
that Joe had dropped.

Woof! His mother growled at him
angrily and gave him a spank that knocked
him head over heels. That would teach
him not to run away while she was asleep!

The children were laughing. They looked
back as their father drove away. They saw
Cuff follow his mother into the woods.

"He ate my cookies," said Joe.

"Just be glad that his mother didn't eat
you," Kathy said.

By watching his mother, Cuff learned which foods are good for bears to eat. They ate roots, beetles, frogs, mice, and ants. Ants tickled Cuffs tongue when he ate them, and they tasted sour — like bear pickles.

One day Cuff chased a mouse into some
bushes. He bumped smack into a fierce male
bear who was taking a nap. The bear
jumped up with an angry growl. He was
bigger than Cuff's mother. He swung his
paw and slapped Cuff over.

He was Cuff's father, but that made no difference. He didn't like cubs!

Cuff ran back to his mother, bawling with fright. The big bear ran after him. His teeth tore out some of Cuff's fur.

Cuff's mother gave him a push to send him up a tree. Then she growled at the male bear and showed her teeth. She was telling him, "Go away! I don't want you near my cub!"

She hit him on the nose. The male bear
slapped her with his paw. Cuff's mother
snatched at his ear with her teeth.

The male bear didn't really want to fight Cuff's mother. He turned and ran off into the woods.

Cuff's mother called Cuff down from the tree. She licked his face and talked to him in soft Mother Bear sounds.

Blueberries are the food that bears love
best of all. Cuff and his mother found a
hillside covered with berry bushes. While
they were there, another bear come out of
the woods. She had two fat cubs. One was
black, and the other had brown fur. But
both of them were black bear cubs.

Cuff's mother and the other bear did not fight. Each knew that the other would not hurt her cubs.

Cuff gave a happy woof. Here were playmates at last!

He hid behind a bush. When Blackie
came near, Cuff jumped out at him.
Brownie ran to help her brother. The three
cubs growled and bit and cuffed, but it
was all in play. When they grew tired,
they fell asleep with their paws around
one another.

Days were growing shorter, and there
was a cold nip to the air. These signs told
bears that it was almost time to den up
for the winter.

Cuff was five times as big as he had
been in spring. But he would not be a

full-grown bear for more than two years. His fur was thick and warm. Under it was a deep layer of fat. This would feed him while he slept through the winter.

One cold cloudy day his mother led him back to their old den. She clawed leaves inside to make a soft bed. Cuff's head nodded sleepily as he watched her.

Gladly he followed his mother in out of the cold. He curled up beside her on the leaves. Soon he was fast asleep.

He did not hear the winter winds
roaring through the woods.

He didn't know that snowflakes were
dancing on the wind.

He would not go outside again until
spring.

KEY WORD LIST

bawling	honeycomb	polliwogs
beetles	hoptoad	roaring
blueberries	gallop	roots
buzzing	growl	snatched
clawed	hopping	snowflakes
climbing	howled	squirrel
cuffed	licked	sunbeams (sunshine)
curled	nipped	swimming
dancing	pawed	tourist
flying	pickles	woodpecker
frogs	playmate	woofed

The Author

VIRGINIA FRANCES VOIGHT has always been interested in natural history and writing. She enjoys researching her material in woodlands of nearby states and writing at her home in Hamden, Connecticut. She is also the author of *Picta the Painted Turtle* and *Patch, a Baby Mink*.

The Artist

SALEM TAMER has been making pictures as far back as he can remember, but his formal art training includes studies at Vesper George School in Boston and the Arts Students League of New York. His illustrations for books and magazines, his advertising art, book jackets, and industrial publications include more than one prize-winning design. He has also illustrated the easy-to-read biographies of *Jefferson Davis, Andrew Jackson* and *John Marshall* for Putnam's.